Moshe's Big Day:
A Lesson in Trust

W I D E Island Publishing

Wide Island Publishing, LLC
First Edition

ISBN 978-1-7373641-1-5 (paperback)
ISBN 978-1-7373641-0-8 (hardback)
ISBN 978-1-7373641-2-2 (eBook)

Scripture quotations are taken from the Holy Bible, New Living Translation, copyright ©
1996, 2004. Used by permission of Tyndale House Publishers, Inc., Carol Stream, Illinois 60188.
All rights reserved.

Logo and book design by Abby Redding
www.abbyredding.com

Published by Wide Island Publishing
www.wideislandpublishing.com

For more information, email: author@wideislandpublishing.com
Visit the website above for a list of future publications and more from Wide Island Publishing

From You, for You, to You... Lord, be glorified!

My Anchor:

Thank you for allowing these sails to catch the Wind
and ride the waves of chasing dreams.
I love you.

Moshe the sheep went outside to play.

It was a beautiful
start to a sunshiny day!

"Hello, Mr. Fox!"
he said, as he passed.

But Fox looked hungry!
Oh no, run fast!

"Good morning, Ms. Bear!"
he said, with a grin.

"Hello, little sheep. Won't you come to my den?"

"My goodness," said Moshe. "This is no place to play. I better go look for a field far away."

So Moshe ran off;
he leaped over briars.

He stomped through
the grass. He pranced
through the flowers.

"I know," thought Moshe.

"My shepherd would say: 'Trust in my voice
when you can't find your way.'"

So Moshe leaned in; he looked past the briars.

He perked up his ears. He gazed through the flowers.

He carried him home and saved the day.

"The world sure is big,
and it's scary some days.

Goodnight, little lamb.

Dear Parents,

I know I don't need to convince you that this world can be a scary place at times. If you're like me, you try not to think about it often, but sometimes even the sunniest days can bring some unexpected reminders. My prayer is that this book will serve as a platform to help you prepare your child for life in this big, scary world. Though the world can be a frightening place, there's One who overcame it and promises to never leave us. His name is Jesus, and this story is meant to point to Him. Thank you for reading it to your child! I hope it's an encouragement to you, too!

Scripture and Story Connections:

In addition to the story, read these Bible verses and
connecting points with your child:

John 10: Just like Moshe listened for his shepherd's voice, we can listen for Jesus's voice. He speaks to us through the Bible and by His Holy Spirit and loves to have a relationship with us! Has God ever spoken to you through the Bible? Ask Him to help you hear what He has to say. Just like Moshe heard his shepherd, you can hear God speak to you, too.

"I am the good shepherd; I know my own sheep, and they know me, just as my Father knows me and I know the Father. So I sacrifice my life for the sheep. I have other sheep, too, that are not in this sheepfold. I must bring them also. They will listen to my voice, and there will be one flock with one shepherd," (John 10:14-16, NLT).

John 16: Moshe saw some scary things, but he remembered that his shepherd would always be looking out for him. His shepherd called his name and was on his way before Moshe even knew it! Jesus will always come after you, too, and he promises never to leave you. When you feel scared or afraid, ask Jesus to help you. You might see or experience some scary things like Moshe, but you can trust in Jesus to help you get through them. And He's bigger and greater than all the scary things in this world!

"I have told you all this so that you may have peace in me. Here on earth you will have many trials and sorrows. But take heart, because I have overcome the world," (John 16:33, NLT).

Romans 5: If something scary happens, does that mean God doesn't love you? The Bible says that God showed us His love by sending Jesus to die on the cross to save us from our sins. He loves you so much that he gave his life for you! Moshe's shepherd really loved Moshe and knew exactly what he needed. God knew what we needed, too – Jesus! So when you go through scary things, you never have to wonder if God loves you. Remember that Jesus is safe!

"But God showed his great love for us by sending Christ to die for us while we were still sinners," (Romans 5:8, NLT).

How Many Butterflies Did You Find?

_____

Write your answer here!

There are a total of 17 butterflies!

Made in the USA
Columbia, SC
29 April 2022

59579270R00018